Gym Rats:

First Meet

GYM RATS:

FIRST MEET

MARY REISS FARIAS

Janet Venné, Illustrator

IrisBlu
publishing

Tucson, AZ
IrisBlu Publishing.com

This book is a work of fiction. Names, characters, places and incidents are products of the author's imagination or are used fictitiously. Any resemblance to actual events or locales or persons, alive or deceased, is entirely incidental.

First printing 2016

ISBN 978-0-9843406-6-8

For Morgan

This book is dedicated to all my little level 3s starting their first year of competitive gymnastics.

INTRODUCTION

Welcome to the fourth book in the *Gym Rats* series! If you'll remember from the previous books, best friends Morgan and Madison are gymnasts and they love gymnastics. The two girls can't wait to get to the gym and are always making up routines. Because the two of them can't get enough gymnastics, their coach, Deb, gives them nicknames: Madison is "Gym" and Morgan is "Rat." *Moving Up* leaves off with Morgan and Madison moving up to competitive team.

First Meet continues the Gym Rats' story and takes on the same format as the first three books in the series. After Morgan and Madison's story, you will find the "Coach's Corner" and the "Drills to Skills" pages where technique and drills are discussed. I hope that you find these sections useful in the gym. Also, at the very end of the book is the glossary. While reading, you will come across certain words in **bold** print. These words are defined in the glossary.

My hope is that you've enjoyed the *Gym Rats* books so far and will like *First Meet* just the same – or even more!

Thank you for reading!
Mary Reiss Farias

Chapter 1

Big Day

Tomorrow

We were finally settled in the hotel after dinner. It was cool because Allison and I had our own room in the suite. Jack slept on a pull-out bed in Mom and Dad's room. We had to get up early in the morning for the meet, so the two of us went to bed early. While we were laying there waiting to fall asleep, I said, "Al, do you like competing?"

"Yeah, I like it," she said. "But I like working skills better."

"Is it scary?"

"No, not really *scary*," she said. "It's different than that. I get nervous to compete, but I'm not *scared*."

"Is it because there are all those people watching?" I asked.

"No, it's not really the crowd that makes me nervous. It's more just because I'm being judged. I want to do better than the meet before, and that makes me nervous."

"Oh," I said. "Are you nervous that you won't make it to **Regionals**?" I asked.

"Good night, girls," Mom called from the other room.

"Good night," we said.

"Be sure to get some good sleep tonight, Al. Big day tomorrow."

"I will," answered Al. "Night."

"And no," Al whispered. "I'm making it to Regionals tomorrow. Night!"

I smiled and thought about what Al said. I thought that it might be scary to get up in front of hundreds of people and compete - especially on beam. But that didn't seem to phase Al. It made sense that the judges made her nervous. I think I would be nervous too to do a routine in front of them. But what I didn't really understand was why she was nervous to do better than the last time. I mean, what did it matter if she beat herself? I thought about this as I drifted to sleep.

Chapter 2

STATE MEET

We got up early. Al woke up at six so she could shower and get ready for her **State** meet. I took my shower the night before so she could have the bathroom all to herself to do her hair and everything. I opened my eyes and saw Al's competition leotard hanging on the door handle. It was so pretty with sequins and a glitter "TGC" on the back. I couldn't wait to compete and have my own competition leotard!

When Al was all finished getting ready, we went to breakfast. We went to a cool breakfast place where they made scrambled tofu instead of eggs. I had a breakfast burrito with scrambled tofu and meatless sausage in it. I had never had scrambled tofu before. It was pretty good! Al had a coconut yogurt and granola parfait with fruit. Mom said that a breakfast burrito would be too heavy for her before the meet. She was right; I was full after that!

We got to the meet in plenty of time for Al to relax a little bit before open warm-ups started. All the TGC girls waited in the lobby for the whole team and the coaches to arrive and then they walked in together. They looked perfect in their matching warm-up suits and their hair done up. They chattered about how long it took their mom to do their hair and what type of glitter they used. Then Scott came in.

"All right, girls! Are we ready to go in?"

"Yes!" the girls said in unison. All the girls said good bye to their parents and were wished good luck. Then they all walked into the gym together. I watched them as they walked through the doors to the big gym. My stomach flipped for them!

Mom, Dad, Jack and I walked in through the big double-door entrance to the gym. The gym was huge. There were balloons and decorations all over welcoming teams from across the state, there were two sets of brand-new equipment, and there were nervous gymnasts grouped in their teams ready to warm up everywhere. TGC met over by one of the vault runways. Coach Scott went over to the head table to sign in and get the coach's packet. The girls started warming up their ankles with the bands that we used in the gym for ankle **injury prevention**.

"Let's go find a seat, Morgan," I hardly heard my mom say. Jack gave me a shove from behind.

"Stop it," I barely was able to say. I was in complete awe. I couldn't *wait* to compete in a meet like this!

I sat on the bleachers with my parents and Jack watching all the **level 8s** do their **open warm-up** before they marched in. All the TGC parents and fans sat together so we could all be loud when we cheered for our girls.

During march-in, all the teams across the state were introduced. There were a lot of them! Then they played the National Anthem. I know I was supposed to be looking at the flag, but I couldn't help but watch all the TGC girls put one hand on their heart and the other on their teammate's shoulder next to them. It was awesome!

Al rotated to floor first. She warmed up everything really well and I've never seen her do such a good **double full**! I watched her as she waited for her turn to compete. When the gymnast before her was up, Al went over to the side of the floor where she was going to start her routine, and she closed her eyes. I knew she was visualizing herself doing her floor routine. The music stopped and the crowed cheered. Al was next.

I loved Allison's floor routine. She was such a good dancer and her music had a really strong beat. The music started. Al started dancing. She moved into the corner and did an awesome double full. Her **leap pass** was to **full split**, and she did some more dance to the corner. Her second tumbling pass, which was a **back half, punch front**, was great, too! She took one step on the **blind landing**. She did some more dance, a **one-and-a-half turn**, and then went into the corner for her third and final pass. She did a super high **full twist**. It was awesome! Then she finished her routine. The TGC crowed erupted. "Yeah, Al!" I cheered. All smiles, Allison stood up and saluted to the judges. She ran off the floor and Scott was waiting with a high-five and a big hug. What a great way to start the meet!

After floor the team rotated to vault. Al warmed up her **pike Tsuk**. Her vault got so much better since last year. Last year she did a **tuck Tsuk**, and sometimes didn't stay on her feet in meets. This year, she **upgraded** her vault and it just got way better. But I was just her sister. What did I know?

It turned out that Al was first up on vault. She stood at the end of the **runway**. The **head judge** raised the green flag, and Al saluted. She stepped onto the runway, took a deep breath, and started running. "Come on, Al!" I yelled. She ran down the runway, hit the board, blocked off the horse, and did a sky-high pike Tsuk. It was so high even the judges were wide-eyed when Al stuck the landing. She saluted the judges and stood by Scott to see if she should compete another one. Al's score must have been a good one, because Scott patted her on the back and Al went to go put her **grips** on.

We all waited in anticipation to see what her score was. Then it flashed - in all it's glory - a 9.45. "Wow! Way to go, Al!" I screamed. All of Allison's teammates hugged and congratulated her. That was awesome. I can't believe Al got such a high score! But there was only a short time to celebrate - it was time for Al's group to rotate to bars.

Al and the rest of her **rotation** warmed up on bars. It was crazy. After almost each one of the girls, the coaches had to rush and and **set** the bars to the next girl's **setting**. They were fast! The time seemed to zip by so fast that it was hard to tell if Al had a good warm-up or not. I did see her do a full routine, though, so that was good.

Almost the whole group went on bars before Allison was up. She stood back and cheered for all the girls as they went through their routines. Just like on floor, when the gymnast before Al was up, Al closed her eyes and visualized her routine. She dipped her hands in the chalk one last time, and was ready to go. She stood in front of the low bar. The judge raised the flag and Allison saluted. She looked at the low bar and started her routine. **Glide kip**, **cast handstand**, **half pirouette**, kip, **squat-on**, **long-hang kip**, cast handstand, **free hip handstand**, **giant**, giant, **layout flyaway**. It looked great! Al even stuck her landing. There were high-fives all around!

The girls were smiling and chatting as they made their way over to the beam area. They all started warming up their skills on any mat they could find. They even practiced on the hard floor without mats! That was crazy to me, watching them do **back handsprings** and **switch leaps** on the hard floor. Then all of a sudden, it was time for the girls to take turns warming up on the beam. Finally it was Allison's turn. She started with her **full turn**, then moved on to her **series**. She did a **back handspring step out** for a warm-up, then she walked forward to do her series. Back handspring, back handspring…BIG wobble, and she landed on the mat to the side of the beam. She jumped right back up and did her leap pass, then she warmed up her dismount. I saw Scott motion for Al to jump up and do another series. This time, she didn't even touch her feet on the beam on her second back handspring. Her time was up and she didn't even stick a series! She walked over to Scott with a nervous look on her face. Scott looked calm and I watched him talk Al into believing that she had her series. After they finished talking, Allison found a quiet spot and sat down and closed her eyes. She was visualizing her series.

Scott came over to Allison when the competitor before her was saluting to the judge. Al stood up and looked him in the eyes and nodded. She took a deep breath, circled her arms, and rolled her head from side to side. Finding a small pile of chalk on the mat at the end of the beam, Al dipped her hands and feet in. She was ready. The girl before her dismounted and saluted to the judges. It was Al's turn.

Allison stood next to the beam, facing the judges, waiting to salute. She stood there for what seemed like forever. The judges wouldn't stop talking about the competitor before her! What was Al thinking about while she waited? I wondered if she was thinking about her series and the fact that she hadn't stuck one in warm-ups. She must have been going crazy inside - I know I was! Finally, the judges sat down and the head judge raised the green flag. Al saluted. She turned to face the beam and mounted.

Dancing a bit before her full turn, she looked confident. Next it was time to do her series. She stepped forward, stood tall with her arms by her ears, and swung backwards into a back handspring step out, then immediately went back into another back handspring step out. Both feet landed on the beam. Her arms and chest came up quickly and she turned sideways. She lifted a leg as she tried to catch her balance. She circled her arms. I could barely watch! Then all of a sudden, her foot found the beam again and Al steadied herself with her arms out in front of her. She turned the right way again, faced the end of the beam, and finished as though nothing happened. "Woo hoo!" Mom yelled next to me. Al went through the rest of her routine with hardly any wobbles. She set up for her dismount - round-off layout. Stick. Wow! What a great routine! We all cheered and clapped. Scott and her teammates gave Allison high-fives. Al looked over at us, wiped her hand across her forehead and looked as though she was saying, "Phew!"

Allison looked relieved as she sat with her teammates watching the rest of the competitors finish up competing. Before awards, Al came over to us. "Great job, Honey!" Mom and Dad said.

"Yeah, nice work, Al!" I smiled.

Jack even said, "That was a decent effort."

On to awards, Al and the rest of the TGC team sat in front of the awards stand waiting for their age groups. Vault was first, and Allison won with her awesome vault! She was State Champ! She got a few more awards as time went on, and then they announced the Regional qualifiers.

They called Al's name - she made it! I couldn't wait to compete and do what Al just did!

Chapter 3

INSPIRED

While we drove home from Al's state meet, I wrote to Gym in our notebook.

Dear Gym,

It was soooo awesome to watch Al and the other optionals compete at State! Allison did great - SHE WON VAULT!! I can't wait till I can do a Tsuk. Wouldn't that be so cool to be able to flip like that? And she won! I can't WAIT to compete and win a gold medal!

After Al's meet, we stayed to watch the level 9s and 10s compete, too. OH MY GOSH. THEY ARE SO GOOD! It was like watching the Olympics! Just imagine a whole meet full of Liz and Beccas!

I'm ready to get back to the gym and work REALLY hard - I want to compete this fall and do really well. I can't wait to work out and get some more skills and work our routines! I'll show you the video of Allison's vault tomorrow at the gym. It was sooooo good! All right. I have to go now. We are on our way back home from the meet. See you tomorrow!

—RAT

Mom, Dad, Jack, Allison and I put our bags in the back of the SUV and piled in. "Buckle up," Mom called. We all clicked into place. All the way home, as Jack and Al listened to music on their phones, I looked out the window and thought about gymnastics. My best friend, Madison, and I were just invited to be on competitive team. Our first meet would be in the fall, so we were learning our routines right now. Pretty soon would be our critique meet, where a judge would come in and judge our routines and tell us what we needed to improve in order to do well during the season. My palms sweated as I thought about competing. I couldn't wait to get back in the gym!

Chapter 4

Do It Right

Gym and I met at the locker room door five minutes before practice started. I handed her the notebook. "How was the meet?" Gym asked.

"It was so awesome!" I answered. "I wrote all about it in the notebook."

"Level 3s! Time for practice!" we heard Coach Stephanie yell from the gym. Gym and I ran out to the floor. "Line up on the white line."

We all lined up shoulder-to-shoulder and stood like gymnasts, looking at Coach Stephanie. "Okay, girls. We will be working hard on our routines from today on until the critique meet. We have eight weeks of practice until we have to go in front of a judge for the first time. You will be working together as a team, and we will be making sure you all understand the routines and requirements for level 3. Now is the time for you to step up and work hard to make the most of your first competitive season. We are excited to coach you through your first season, and I hope you're excited too! Ok, let's warm up. Today, we will be doing the meet warm-up, which we will be doing as a team when we go to meets."

Coach Stephanie led us through our meet warm-up: jumping jacks, running in place with high knees, bootie kickers, mountain climbers, and a series of stretches. Each of us took turns counting each exercise. And then one of us led stretch. It was pretty cool!

We went right to our first event after warming up. It was vault. We began with our vault **complex**, which was a series of running **drills** and body position drills that we needed to have good vaults. After that we worked on our **handstand flat backs**.

After vault, we went to beam. Again, we worked on our complex. The complex focused on the first half of our beam routine. That meant we worked on walks and body positions that we needed for the first half of our routine. Then our beam workout focused on actually doing the first half of our beam routine correctly. I felt so important up there actually doing my routine!

We had a quick five-minute break where we ate a piece of fruit, and then we went to bars. Of course, we started with our complex. The bar routine was hard. We had to do a good glide swing, a **front hip circle**, and a **front mill circle**! But the point of the complex was to make all those skills actually look good. It wasn't enough just to do the skills anymore. Judges wanted to see us do the skills right!

Chapter 5

FREAKING OUT

We spent most of the summer working our routines and making sure that we hit all the requirements. Allison's group finished their post-season meets, and I watched them in the gym as they got to work the new skills that they wanted to master for the next level. Al was working cool skills like **standing back tucks** on beam, a double full on floor, and **Yurchenko** layouts on vault. And don't even get me started on bars. She was working **blind changes**, **release moves** and **double back flyaways**! It was amazing, and it looked like so much fun!

As we went through the summer perfecting our routines, I didn't want to admit it, but I was getting a little bit bored with only doing routines. Me? Bored of gymnastics? I felt ashamed, and I didn't tell anyone - not even Gym. I think Coach Deb and Coach Stephanie must have sensed something in me (or even in all of us!) and when we went in for practice that day, Deb said, "Okay, level 3s! Go and sit down by the mat. We are going to have a little chat before practice!"

"Are we in trouble?" asked Amber.

"No, you're not in trouble," Coach Stephanie said with a smile. "Sit down and listen."

"Girls, we only have two weeks left before our critique meet," Deb said.

"What's a critique meet?" Leslie asked.

"It's a day when we invite a judge to come in to the gym and watch all of our routines. Then she will tell you what you need to work on before the first official meet."

"Cool!" I said.

"Scary!" said Gym.

"It shouldn't be scary," said Deb. "We are using it as practice for when real competitions begin. No one expects you to be perfect, but we *do* want to do is show you what it is like to be in a meet, so you know what to expect when the season starts."

I looked over at Gym. She was looking down at her feet. I could tell she was already getting nervous.

"To prepare for our critique meet," Deb continued, "we are going to practice our **meet warm-up**, our open warm-up, and our **timed**

warm-ups. That way, when you get to a meet, you'll know exactly what to expect."

"Don't worry, Madison," said Stephanie. "You'll be fine. We are all in it together."

"Okay," answered Gym.

"Any questions?" No one raised her hand, probably because none of us had any idea what was coming next. So we just waited to do what we were told. "All right. Let's do the TGC Meet Warm-up."

We all stood in a circle and we all did jumping jacks. Amber counted. We went around the circle and did different things to warm-up together as a team. It was my turn in the circle when we got to the stretching part, so I led the team in stretching. After that, Deb told us to get a drink and line up on the white line for Open warm-up.

Open warm-up was where we did some basics and routine skills across the floor. It got us warmed up mostly for beam and floor routines. It was the part of the meet right before we rotated to our first competition event. We started with high kicks. "Tight arms, girls! Remember that you are at a meet and judges and other competitors are watching you!" Deb said.

"Judges are watching warm-ups?" asked Gym with wide eyes as I got to the other side of the floor with her.

"I guess they do sometimes," I said.

"I don't know if I'm ready for this," she said.

"You'll be okay," I said. "Allison said the judges aren't that scary."

"She's been competing forever," Gym responded. "Of course they're not scary anymore for her." I didn't know what else to say. Besides, it was my turn to do my **handstand forward roll**.

After practice, Mom picked Al and me up. "How was practice?" she asked.

Allison gave her normal, "Fine."

I followed suit and mumbled, "Fine," too.

"You okay Morgan?" Mom asked.

"Yeah. We're just getting ready for our critique meet, and Gym seems really scared. She's not herself, and it's really weird. I've never seen her like this."

"She's just nervous," Mom said. "Once you kids get familiar with competing, she will be fine. Sometimes it makes some people more nervous than others. Are you nervous?"

"Well, I wasn't until Madison started freaking out," I said. "Now I'm thinking that I should be more worried about all this."

"Don't think about it too much. Your coaches are preparing you the best they can for meets. If I remember correctly, they go over pretty much everything with you in the weeks leading up to your critique meet and first meet. They're really good at making you feel comfortable with the new experience."

"Okay," I said. Even though I thought Gym was making too much out of this, it still made think that I should be more nervous than I was. Was there a reason why she was so scared? Did she know something that I didn't know? Maybe she would write something in the notebook about it and then I could understand better.

Chapter 6

We Are Not In a Fight

At practice the next day, Gym gave me the notebook. "Here you go," she said. She stuck it in my hands. "I really didn't have that much time to write in it. We were in the back yard all day and night having a cookout and a bonfire."

41

"That's okay," I said. That was weird. Gym usually called me over to hang out when their family was cooking out and hanging out in the back yard. She only had one brother and he was way older then her, so she didn't have anyone to really play with. Maybe they had cousins over or something. But even then, she usually invited me.

Gym went to fill her water bottle before practice. I took a quick peek at the notebook.

Dear Morgan,

I really don't have much to write about tonight. I'll see you at practice tomorrow.

—Madison

Again, all this was so weird. First of all, she didn't invite me to her house, then she called me "Morgan" and herself "Madison." We never did that - especially in the notebook! And then she couldn't write about *anything*? I mean, I *know* she was thinking about gymnastics and judges and meets. And she couldn't write about *anything*? I was starting to get angry at *Madison*.

I went out to the gym. We got in a circle and started our meet warm-up and went along through practice. Warm-ups, routines, warm-ups routines. I was starting to get excited about the critique meet!

Madison didn't talk to me one bit at practice. She was quiet and didn't talk to anyone, actually. The team was stretching together after practice, and everyone was gabbing about the critique meet coming up - everyone but Madison.

"I hope the judge is nice," said Amber.

"I wonder if she'll wear her blue uniform?" asked Leslie.

"I wonder if she'll talk to us?" I asked.

"All right, girls, it's time to go!" Deb called to us. We all filed into the locker room.

Gym was already leaving as I walked in the door to the locker room. "Bye, Gym," I said."

"Bye," she said as the door closed behind her.

"What's up with her?" Amber asked me.

"Are you guys in a fight?" asked Leslie.

"She's fine, and no, we are not in a fight," I said defensively. At least I didn't think so…

Chapter 7

THANKS FOR
NOTHING

I went home again concerned about my best friend. She was really silent about everything, and I just didn't get it. After my shower and dinner, I went and knocked on Al's door. "Yeah?" Al yelled over the music she had playing. As I started talking the volume went down.

"Al? It's me. Can I talk to you for a second?" I asked through the door.

"Come in," she answered. I opened the door and she plopped down on the bed. "What's up?"

"That's what I need to find out," I said. "Madison is acting really weird and I don't know why. She won't talk to me, and she won't even write in the notebook. I know something is bothering her, but she won't tell me. I don't know what I did to make her act this way."

"Well, maybe it's not about you this time, Morgan. Maybe there's something going on in her life that doesn't involve you, and she doesn't want to talk about it."

"But we tell each other *everything*," I protested.

"Well, maybe she just doesn't want to talk about it. Sometimes people don't want to talk about their problems."

"But what if I can help?" I asked. I was getting mad at Al. What was she talking about? Gym and I were best friends. We didn't have any secrets from each other. We were like sisters!

"Sometimes kids can't help other kids," Al said. "I'm sorry if I sound harsh, but it's the truth."

This talk didn't help at all. "Ok, thanks..." I said. As I closed the door, I added, "...for nothing." What did Al know anyway? I went to write in the notebook.

Dear Gym,

How are you doing? It really seems like there is something wrong with you that you're not telling me. Did I do something to you that I didn't realize? Are you ok? You just don't seem the same, and I want to try to help you out if I can.

Can you believe the critique meet is in two days? It's crazy that it has gone this fast! I think that I'm ready to go, but I don't know how I'll do. How about you? Do you feel ready? Ok, I'll see you at practice tomorrow for our last day before the critique meet!

-Rat

P.S. Feel better!

Chapter 8

SWEATY PALMS

I walked into the locker room, and Madison was putting her gym bag in her locker. "Hi, Gym," I said, unsure of if I was going to get an answer.

"Hi, Rat," I heard.

"How are you doing?" I asked, hoping to get another answer.

"I'm okay," Gym said. "I'm tired," she added.

"Why are you so tired?" I asked.

"We've been doing a lot of family things," she said.

"Oh," I answered. "Here's the notebook. Can you believe that we only have one practice left before the critique meet?"

"I know," she said. "It's crazy!"

This was good. Even though she was tired, Gym started to sound like herself a little bit. Like she actually liked gymnastics, and *me*.

"Level 3s!" we heard from the gym. "Time to go!"

We ran out to the floor. Deb and Stephanie were waiting there for us. "Today is our last practice before the critique meet. Start with the meet warm-up. Amber, you count."

Amber started counting jumping jacks. We all did them together.

We took turns leading and then did our open warm-up. Deb told us to go to vault first. We each did our routines on each event with our teammates and coaches sitting and watching us. I felt a little nervous each time I did my routines. It really felt like all eyes were on me! But it wasn't that bad. Hopefully the critique meet wouldn't be that much worse.

At the end of practice, Deb said, "Girls, come and sit down. Let's have a chat about tomorrow." We all ran over to the mat and sat down. "Nice workout today. You all look like you're ready to go out there tomorrow and see what the judge has to say about your routines. Now, remember, we don't expect you to be perfect, but we do expect you to learn from your mistakes. That's how we get better. The judge will be here to tell you what you could be doing better to make your first meet and the rest of your season go well."

"Okay, there are some things that we need to go over before tomorrow," said Stephanie. "First, get here on time. We start at twelve o'clock sharp. Just like a meet, we will not wait for anyone if she is late. If you're late, you'll just have to catch up."

Gym and I looked at each other with wide eyes. "Let's get here at eleven-thirty," I whispered. Gym nodded and looked back at Stephanie.

"Make sure your hair us up and out of your face. Use hairspray! We don't have time during a meet to be fixing everyone's hair. Also, wear only one pair of small earrings, if you have pierced ears. And take off your finger- and toenail polish!"

"Wear your TGC leotard, and eat healthy meals between now and then," added Deb. "Any questions?" she asked.

No one raised her hand. I felt a twinge in my stomach and my hands started to sweat a little. I was getting nervous!

As Gym and I walked out of the locker room to the lobby, I saw my mom and Gym's mom talking. My mom nodded and rubbed Gym's mom's back. "Let's go," her mom said to Gym.

"Bye," both of us said to each other.

When we got to the car, Mom said, "Madison is coming over this afternoon and will spend the night with us. We will take her to the critique meet with us tomorrow."

"Cool! Why?" I asked, realizing that if we did that, Gym's mom and dad wouldn't be there to watch her compete.

"Madison's parents just can't make it, so we're helping them out," Mom answered.

"Oh," I said. I knew better than to ask any more questions.

Chapter 9

THREE FALLS?!

Gym came over later that afternoon. I was reading a book by the upstairs window where I could see the driveway. I saw Gym's mom pull up in her blue SUV. I slammed my book closed and ran down the stairs. Before Gym's mom could ring the doorbell, I opened the door. "Hi!" I said.

"Hello, Morgan," Gym's mom said. "How are you doing?"

"Fine, thank you," I replied, reaching for Gym's overnight bag. My mom came to the door behind me.

"Come on in, ladies," she said. Gym and her mom stepped into the front entryway. Gym wasn't as excited to run away with me as she usually was. She stuck by her mom's side until our moms were finished talking, then her mom gave her a big hug and kiss.

"I'll see you tomorrow, Kiddo. Everything will be okay. Good luck in your critique meet! Morgan's mom and dad are going to record it for us."

"Okay, Mom. I love you."

"I love you too, Honey." She turned and left. Of course it wasn't weird that Gym's mom wanted to give her daughter a hug and a kiss before she left, but it was weird that Gym didn't do it sooner so we could go off and play. There was definitely something going on.

"Do you want to practice our beam routine downstairs?" I asked as we put Gym's stuff in my room.

"Okay," Gym answered. She followed me to the basement. We stretched a little bit and then started working our beam routine. We gave each other scores. We practiced saluting for the "judge" and we pretended we were in a real meet. I really tried hard not to wobble, but it was tough!

"Dinner time!" we heard my mom call from the kitchen. Gym and I ran up the stairs and washed up. Then we went to the kitchen. It smelled so good! My mom made whole-grain spaghetti with marinara sauce. There was a huge salad in the middle of the table, a bunch of fresh fruit and some whole-grain bread on the sides. All the water glasses were full. "Come on in and sit down," Mom said. Mom, Dad, Allison, Jack, Gym and I all sat at the table together and ate.

"Do you know why this is a good meal to have tonight?" Dad asked?

"Because it tastes good?" I said.

"Well, of course," laughed Dad. "But that's not it. It's got some great complex carbohydrates for you two girls so you can have lots of energy for tomorrow's meet."

"Critique meet," I corrected him. "It's not a real meet yet."

"True. But you do have to treat it like one," Dad said. "That way you'll get the most out of the experience. You want to make sure that you go into it just as you would a regular competition. That's what it's for: to get you ready for the real thing."

I felt the twinge come back into my stomach and my palms started to sweat again. I was getting nervous again! I put my fork down.

"What's wrong, Morgan?" Mom asked.

"I'm not very hungry anymore," I said.

"You're just nervous," Al said. "You'll be fine. It's not that big of deal."

"Allison, I seem to remember you at your first critique meet. You were so nervous that you made me do your hair three times until it was absolutely perfect!"

"Well, I had to look good!" Al answered.

We all laughed. "Were you really nervous, Al?" I asked.

Allison shrugged. "Yes she was," Mom answered for her. "She couldn't sleep the night before and kept calling me in to her room. First she wanted water, then she wanted another stuffed animal, then her pillow wasn't comfortable. She was a bundle of nerves!"

"I did all right," Allison said.

"If you call falling off the beam three times 'all right,'" chimed in Jack.

Allison shot him an angry glare across the table.

"Woah," Gym whispered.

"You fell off beam *three times*?" I asked, almost yelling.

"Shhh..." Mom said.

"Yes. Yes I did. I fell off the beam on my mount, my handstand, and my leap. There. Are you happy? No, I didn't do great, but I did learn what it was like to compete."

"See?" said Dad. "That's what I mean. You have to use tomorrow as a learning tool. You're going to get nervous, but that's okay. You're not going to be perfect, and that's perfectly fine. Use tomorrow to see what it feels like to compete."

"That's right," said Mom. "You girls go out there and do what you've been practicing. See what you can do, and then you'll talk to the judge and she will tell you what you need to improve on."

I heard a clank on the plate next to me. Gym had put her fork down too. "Okay, five more bites for each of you," Mom said. "I'll leave the fruit out for when you get hungry later tonight."

Gym and I finished our five bites and went up to my room. I helped Gym unroll her sleeping bag. We sat on the floor and finally started to talk.

"Why do you have to stay with us tonight?" I asked. "Don't get me wrong. I'm thrilled to have you here. I'm just wondering what happened?"

"My grandpa's really sick. He went into the hospital a few days ago and he isn't getting any better. My parents had to host my family that is in from out of town and also help my grandma. They couldn't do that *and* go to my meet tomorrow, so they're skipping my meet."

"Oh, I'm sorry. But why didn't you tell me before?"

"Because my mom didn't want to make a huge deal out of it so I wouldn't freak out. But I knew something was going on and I finally asked her what was happening. And she told me." Gym got really quiet and wiped a tear from her eye. "I just hope he's going to be okay," she said.

I didn't know what to say anymore. So I just gave her a hug. As much as I hated to admit it, Al was right. Sometimes kids can't help other kids.

"Time for bed, girls!" Mom called from the stairway. "Brush your teeth and get ready for bed. You have a big day tomorrow!"

Chapter 10

CRITIQUE MEET

"Good morning!" Mom said as she came in my room and opened the shades. The morning light came in through the windows and hit me right in the eyes.

"Mom!" I complained. "That's too bright!"

"Too bad, so sad," Mom answered. "Now get up. I've got breakfast waiting for you downstairs. Then you ladies have to get ready for your competition!"

Gym and I sat up in bed wide-eyed and looked at each other. The critique meet! We got up and followed my mom downstairs to the breakfast table.

There was oatmeal, berries, apples, bananas, and toast with peanut butter on the table. It all looked so good! "Here you go, girls," Mom said. "Take what you want. I'll pack a snack for each of you to keep in your gym bags."

We ate our oatmeal and fruit and then went upstairs to get ready. Gym took a shower first. While she was in there, Al came into my room.

"Good luck today," she said.

"Thanks, Al." She started to go downstairs. "Al? How nervous were you for your first critique meet?"

"Well, I wasn't nervous *before* the meet, but I got really nervous once we started," she said.

"Oh," I said. "Why do we get so nervous?"

"It's just a natural thing. You have to go up in front of people and show off what you do. If you weren't nervous, you wouldn't be normal," she said.

"Well, at least I'm normal I guess," I said.

"You'll be fine," Al said. "Good luck!"

"Thanks," I muttered. I just wasn't so sure. I mean, what if I fell off the beam on every skill? What if I didn't make any of my skills? What if I forgot my routines? Ahhh!

I snapped back to reality when Gym came into my room wrapped in a towel. "All yours," she said.

"Okay." I got up off my bed and went to take a shower.

After my shower, I opened the door to my room and Gym was in her leotard going through her beam routine dance. "Oh, hi," she said. "I was just practicing. I don't want to forget my routine!"

"Me either!" I agreed. I put my leotard on and joined her in doing our dance. "You know what?" I said.

"What?" asked Gym.

"I never thought about it, but these are official leotards! They're not just practice leotards; we are competing in them today!"

"Not with your hair like that, you're not." My mom stood in the doorway with her hands on her hips. "Girls, get in the bathroom. We need to do your hair and get to the gym."

When we piled out of the car, the parking lot was full of cars. "I don't remember Saturdays being this busy," I said.

"Well, you'll have an audience today," Dad said.

"Great," I said.

"You'll be fine," Mom said. "Just keep your wits about you."

Gym and I rushed to get out of the car. "Good luck!" Mom, Dad, Al and Jack yelled as we ran to the gym door.

I turned around and gave them all a wave. In the locker room, all the level 3s, 4s and 5s were putting their stuff in their lockers. Everyone had their team practice leotard on, and their hair pulled back tight in buns or curled in ponytails. Nervous chatter about how their hair looked filled the room. Some girls were spraying last-minute glitter in their teammates' hair.

Coach Stephanie appeared at the locker room door. "Time to go, girls!"

I looked at Gym. She looked back at me with wide eyes. "Let's do it," she said. I nodded as we followed the rest of our teammates out the door into the gym.

There was a table and chairs set up by each event for the judges. There were also extra chairs lined up along the edge of the gym so family members could sit and watch the critique meet. I scanned the crowed for my parents and found them sitting next to Dakota's parents. Al was sitting on the floor with her teammates while Deb went over how they were going to help flash scores and time routines. Jack was in the lobby reading a book.

That was still a weird sight for me to see him reading and sitting quietly. But since my mom changed how we ate, he was actually really normal!

My mom spotted me looking for them and waved. I waved back. Just then, Stephanie called to us to get in a circle to start the meet warm-up. Angie, one of the level 5s, led the warm-up. We all followed by starting our jumping jacks all at the same time, as a team.

As we stretched, Deb came over with the two judges. "Here they come," Gym whispered to me. I looked up. They were standing right over me.

"Girls, the is Judge Jill and Judge Brooke. They will be judging your critique meet today."

"Hi, ladies," Judge Jill said.

"Hi," we all said in unison.

"Good luck!" Judge Brooke smiled. They walked over to the vault area and talked to Deb.

We finished our warm-up and we went to vault. The level 3s went first because we used a **pit mat** instead of a **vault table**. We started our timed warm-up. Deb started the timer. We had a certain amount of time to warm up before we competed. We ended up getting about three vaults in before time was up. Stephanie was at the end of the runway with our order. Leslie was first. She looked nervous! Stephanie stood at the end of the runway with us and Deb was at the pit mat. She joked with the judges. How could she be so easygoing with them?

The judge raised her hand and Leslie saluted. She stood on the runway and took a deep breath. She ran, hit the board, and did her handstand flat back. It was pretty good! She sat on the mat and stood up on the floor and started to walk back. "SALUTE!" Deb and Stephanie yelled at her.

Leslie stopped in her tracks and said, "Oops!" Her face red, she turned around and saluted the judges. She smiled. She came back to the end of the runway and performed her second vault.

Amber was next, and I was after her. Gym was after me. Amber was already at the end of the runway, and Stephanie motioned for me to come over to her. "Come on, Amber!" yelled

Stephanie. "All right, Rat. Are you ready for this?"

"Yup," I answered. "I hope I don't forget to salute," I said.

"You won't. You'll do fine. Just do your vault like you normally do in the gym. You can do it." Amber came back to the end of the runway for her second vault. "Good one, Amber. Do it again," said Stephanie. After Amber took off, Stephanie said, "You're up, Rat." She nudged me over to the runway. "Gym, come on over!"

My stomach flipped a little bit, and my hands started to sweat. I took a deep breath and waited for the judge to raise her hand. I picked my wedgie. *Don't forget to salute. Don't forget to salute*, I said to myself. The judge's hand went up. I saluted. *I'm saluting to a judge for the first time!* I thought to myself. I stepped to the center of the runway and made sure I was standing at my starting place. *Don't forget to salute. Don't forget to salute*, I thought again as I ran down the runway. I hit the board and did my handstand flat back. *Don't forget to salute*. I stood up off the mat and faced the judges. I saluted and started to walk back.

"Morgan!" I head Deb say. "You have to hit the handstand before you fall to your back. Just do it like you do in practice."

I nodded and trotted back to the end of the runway. "Come on, Rat! Hit that handstand!" Stephanie said. The judge raised her hand. I saluted back, stepped to the center of the runway, and started to run. I hit the board and did my vault. I landed on my back on the mat, and stood up. I looked at the judges and saluted again. I remembered!

I heard the crowed clap and cheer. I ran back to the end of the runway to join my team. I sat down just as Gym saluted. "Come on, Gym!" I yelled. I looked down by the judges.

Al was down there flashing scores. She flipped the flasher to the right score and held it up. 8.35. Not bad!

The 3s finished vault, and the 4s and 5s vaulted while we went over to bars to warm up. We only got two turns on bars to get all of our skills in. It was really quick! As soon as one person got off the bar, the next person had to jump for her glide swing.

After the judges finished with vault, they came over and judged us on bars. Amber was first. She waited for the judge to raise her hand. She saluted and did her routine. She barely made her front hip circle, but she made her routine. After she saluted, she came back and sat down with the rest of us. "Phew! I barely made that one!"

"Good job, Amber," I said.

"Thanks, Rat," she said. Was I crazy? Or were we finally being nice to each other?

Gym was up next, and Dakota was after her. Leslie and Charlotte were up, then Samantha, and I was last. It was tough to wait! When Samantha was up right before me, I went over to Stephanie and listened to what she had to say.

"It's okay to be nervous, Rat, but you have to remember to think about your routine. Don't think about anything else but what you are doing."

"Okay," I said. "Can I chalk up?"

"Of course. Go ahead," she answered.

I stood and waited for the judge to raise her hand. She finally did, and I saluted. While I did my routine, I thought about what skill came next. Glide swing, **pullover**, **single-leg shoot through**… I came to my dismount, and instead of going up on my **under swing**, I shot straight out and landed on my butt. I stood up and picked my wedgie. I walked over to go sit down. "SALUTE!" everyone yelled.

"Oh!" I said and turned and saluted the judges. *Dang it!* I thought. I sat down next to Gym.

"Good job, Rat," Gym said.

"Thanks. But I forgot to salute!"

"You also landed on your butt," Amber reminded me.

I shot her a look. So much for being nice.

Deb called us over to the judges. "While the 4s and 5s are warming up, the judges want to talk to you about your routines," she announced.

"Girls, you did a good job for the beginning of the season," said Judge Brooke said. "The biggest thing for me is to remember your form. You're in level 3 because you have the skills to be in level 3. What will set you apart from the rest of competitors is your form, especially on vault and bars," she explained. "Be sure you hold your leg up nice and tight after your single-leg shoot through and after your mill circle. Judges really want to see that you are in control. But overall, good job, girls," she said with a smile.

While the 4s and 5s competed on bars, we warmed up on beam. Timed warm-up was so stressful! We stood in a line and waited for the girl in front of us to go. As soon as she got off the beam, the next person had to jump up and go. If we stuck our warm-up, we had to go to the end of the line, but if we fell, we had to get another turn in.

It was finally my turn. Gym finished her dismount, and I climbed up. I felt so rushed as I did my handstand. I didn't make it to vertical, and then fell off as I was backing up to do my leap pass. I jumped back up and finished up. I had to get back in line to do another handstand, even though I didn't technically fall on that. But how do you fall walking? My legs were so wobbly - and this was just warm-ups!

We competed one at a time, and we all fell off during our routines at least once. I fell on my arabesque, and Gym fell on her handstand. A few others fell on their cartwheel handstand dismount. They didn't make it over in order to make the quarter turn at the end. I did that in practice a lot, but I made it in the meet.

Next up was floor. We all warmed up together. It went really fast, and before I knew it, I was up! I waited for the music to start, and I did my routine. My routine was actually pretty good, but I ended after the music stopped. Whoops. But honestly, I was just glad to have it over with!

Judge Brooke gave us some more tips for beam and floor while the others warmed up. She told us to show off and to finish each skill before we moved on to the next. We needed to make sure that our arms were in the correct place when they were supposed to be in crown, and when they were supposed to be straight up.

When the judges were finished, Deb and Stephanie brought us together and congratulated us on a job well done. "We will have recaps for you at your next practice," Deb said.

After the meet, I met Mom and Dad in the parent area. "Great job, Morgan," Mom said.

Dad gave me a high-five. "Nice work, Kiddo!"

"Way to go, Rat," added Allison.

I even got a "you didn't fall off the beam as much as Al," from Jack. And Jack got a sock in the arm from Al.

"You did great, too, Madison," Mom said. "Why don't we go out to lunch and celebrate," she added. We all got in the car and headed to a local restaurant that had vegetarian food.

While we waited for our food, Mom got a phone call. "Sure; she can spend the night again, no problem. You take care, Linda. Here's

Madison." Mom handed the phone to Gym and she talked to her mom for awhile, going over what happened at the meet.

Gym and I chatted about the meet in the car on the way home. "I was so nervous!" I said.

"I know, me too. At least the judges were nice," Gym answered.

"Yeah. Are they always nice like that, Al?" I asked my sister.

"No," Allison laughed. "They are usually intimidating! They were just being nice because it was a critique meet. They are way more serious at a real meet."

"Great," I said. "I can't even remember to salute in my own gym. How am I going to remember to salute plus everything else in a real meet?"

"You'll learn," Mom chimed in.

"You'll get used to it," Dad said.

"I guess," I gave Gym an unsure look. I wasn't so confident.

Chapter 11

RECAP

Gym stayed with us until Sunday afternoon when her parents came to pick her up. We spent most of the time in the basement making up beam and floor routines. We did talk a little about the critique meet and how we did, but we got most of that debriefing out in the car and at the restaurant after the meet.

In the locker room before our next practice, Madison handed me the notebook while I was putting my gym bag in my locker. "Here you go, Rat," she said.

"Thanks," I answered as I took it. I opened it to read what she wrote.

Dear Rat,

First, thank you for being such a great friend and having me over while my parents were away. It was the best place I could have been if I couldn't be in my own house. You are definitely my best friend and you always will be!

Can you believe we competed in our first critique meet? It's all becoming so REAL! We're on team and we're COMPETING! It seems like just yesterday we were on pre team learning how to do a front hip circle and putting stars on the star chart. I wonder how different the real first meet will be? I wonder if it will be the same at all? Allison really made me nervous about what she said about judges. What if she's right? What if they really ARE scary at real meets? Eek!

Okay, it's time to go now. Thanks for being there for me, Rat. You're one in a million.

—Gym

"Oh, Gym," I said. "You're welcome. And you can stay with us any time!"

"Thanks," Gym answered back.

"Level 3s! Time for practice!" We heard Stephanie call us from the gym. We all trotted out to the floor. Deb was standing there with a pile of papers on a clipboard.

"Another clipboard?" I whispered to Gym.

"Girls, let's warm up. After we stretch, Coach Stephanie and I will call you over one by one to go over your meet with you. Here is a whiteboard with the conditioning that you need to do while we are talking with your teammates. Please be responsible and diligent gymnasts and work hard."

After our stretch, Gym and I started our **press handstands**. I stood in a straddle and reached my hands to the floor. I leaned my shoulders over my hands and picked my hips up so I was balancing in a straddle position on my hands. Then I slowly closed my legs straight up so I was in a handstand.

"Madison!" Deb called. Gym ran over and sat down on the panel mat with Deb. I looked over at her as Deb talked. I wonder how these talks are going?

I moved on from my press handstands to my **leg lifts** on the **stall bars**. I pretended that the coaches were watching and correcting me. I kept my legs straight and together. It seemed like forever, but finally I heard my name. "Morgan!" Deb called.

I ran over and sat on the panel mat where Gym had been a few minutes earlier. "How do you think you did in the critique meet?" Deb asked.

"I think I did all right," I answered. "But I could have done better."

"That's a good answer," said Deb. "Everyone put in a great effort, and everyone needs to improve. What do you think you could work on?"

"Well...I forgot to salute after my bar routine," I said. "I was thinking about it the whole time, and I still forgot!"

"So you were thinking about saluting while you were doing your routines?" Deb asked.

"Yes I was," I confessed.

"Then you weren't thinking about your routines while you were doing your routines?"

"No I wasn't," I confessed again.

"Okay. The biggest thing that you need to work on is to think about the skill you are doing as you are doing it. Try to remember in your head all the corrections that Stephanie and I give you during practice and think about them while you are performing your routine."

"That makes sense," I said.

"That way, you can make sure that you are focusing on the little things that can make your routine really good or really not-so-good," Deb smiled.

"Okay," I said. "I can do that."

"Good. I want you to concentrate on that during your practices leading up to the first meet. Let's see how your scores improve."

"All right!" I said. I was excited to compete better!

Chapter 12

A Part of the Team

During the practices leading up to the first meet, I thought about the little things while I was doing my routines. It was hard sometimes to think about keeping my legs straight on my handstand on beam when I was a little scared of going over, but I tried as hard as I could. I really wanted to improve my scores!

The meet was coming up closer and closer. The coaches seemed to be a little more insistent that we stay on the beam and connect our bar routines. They seemed like they were getting nervous too!

Two practices before the meet, Deb and Stephanie came out of the office with a big box. Sticking out if it was a bunch of backpacks.

"Girls," Deb said. "Here is your competition gear! Each of you will receive a backpack with your name on it. Inside of the back pack is your competition leotard, your warm-up jacket, and your warm-up pants. There is also a surprise from the booster club."

"Yea!" we all yelled and squealed for joy.

"Just a minute!" Deb said. "The leotard and warm-ups do NOT have your names on them. It is very important that your mom or dad put your name or initials on the tag inside the clothing so they don't get mixed up. With that in mind, please do not take your leotards and warm-ups out of your bag while you are here. Otherwise they could get mixed up. We will call your names and hand them out while you stretch."

Stephanie started reading names off the bags. "Dakota... Madison... Leslie... Amber... Morgan..."

I went up and grabbed my bag. It was a black backpack with silver lettering with "TGC" at the top and "Morgan" down below. It was awesome! When I got back to where I was stretching, I peeked inside and saw my competition leotard and warm-up in there. And down at the bottom was a pair of flip flops tied with different colored ribbons. It was official - I was a part of the team!

"Girls, one more thing before you leave," Deb said. "Because tomorrow is your last practice before the meet, we will be having a meet run-through. Please wear your TGC warm-up leotards with no shorts, and have your hair up as you would in a meet. We will go through your routines just like you would in a meet."

"I just got nervous," Gym whispered to me.

"I know. I'm so excited and nervous all at the same time!" I told her.

After dinner, I sat down at my desk to write in the notebook.

Dear Gym,

It was so exciting to get our competition gear today at gym! I tried my leotard on when I got home and it's so pretty with all the sparkles. I can't wait to wear it at the meet this weekend!

Holy buckets - the meet is this weekend! OUR FIRST MEET IS THIS WEEKEND! Can you believe it? Like you said before, it all seems to be happening so fast. I mean it felt like it took us forEVER to get out of pre team. And now that we're on team, everything is flying by! WE ARE COMPETING THIS WEEKEND! AHHHHH!!!!!

Okay. See you tomorrow at our MEET RUN-THROUGH!

—Rat

Chapter 13

PREPARING

At practice the next day, we did a meet run-though, which means we pretended we were at a meet during practice. We did our meet warm-up, stretched and did our open warm-up across the floor together. Then we went to each event. There we did timed warm-ups and then "competed" with the whole gym watching.

I tried to think about each skill as I did it instead of thinking about making sure I saluted at the end of my routines. I actually did pretty well and didn't fall off beam. So that was good. I think the run-through helped get me ready for the meet.

While we stretched as a team, Deb came over to give us one last pep talk. "Great job tonight, girls. I think you're as ready as you'll ever be for the meet this weekend. You all have come a long way since the critique meet, and you all have worked hard applying our corrections. Keep up the good preparation tonight and tomorrow by eating healthy foods and drinking plenty of water. Remember to eat for the meet - brown rice, vegetables, fruit…"

"Can we bring a snack in our bags?" Dakota asked.

"Please bring a snack in your bags!" said Deb. "Be sure it's something healthy like apple slices, a banana, or some healthy crackers. Be sure to pack a bottle of water, too. Oh! And take off your nail polish! Any other questions?"

No one raised their hand.

"Okay, girls. We will see you on Saturday at the meet! Be sure to have a good breakfast and have your hair done before you get to the meet. Wear your competition leotard and your warm-up."

"Should we wear our flip flops?" Leslie asked.

"Certainly. You can wear your flip flops," Deb smiled. "Good night, girls!"

Chapter 14

THE BIG DAY

It was the night before the meet and my mom was making a special dinner. She asked me earlier in the week what I wanted for dinner the night before the meet - it had to be healthy, of course - and I chose Pad Thai. It's a rice noodle dish with a bunch of vegetables in it, and my mom made a really good peanut sauce with it. It was one of my favorites!

The whole house was smelling delicious when I was in the basement sitting in my splits. My mom wouldn't let me do much on my beam so I wouldn't get hurt before the meet. But she did say that I could sit in my splits until dinner was ready. I was finishing up middles when mom yelled, "Dinner's ready!"

I got out of my splits and put the stopwatch away. I stopped in the bathroom and washed my hands for dinner. When I got there, Dad, Jack and Al were already at the table. We all sat down and ate the wonderful Pad Thai.

"You're sure eating well before the meet, Morgan," Dad said as he took a bite of broccoli.

"I know. Thanks for dinner, Mom," I said.

"You're welcome, Kiddo," Mom smiled. "We want to make sure you get some good energy before your competition. Now, let's finish eating so you can get to bed early. You have a big day tomorrow."

After dinner, I got ready for bed and set out everything I needed for competition tomorrow: competition leotard, matching scrunchie, warm-up jacket and pants, and flip flops. My mom gave me a little bag with extra hair bands, bobby pins, clips, and hairspray. I put that in my backpack along with tissues, hand sanitizer, Band-Aids, athletic tape and my water bottle, which I would fill up in the morning.

"Okay, Morgan, lights out," Mom said as she came into my room.

"I'm just about packed," I said

I got into bed, and Mom tucked me in. "How are you feeling?" she asked.

"A little nervous," I said. "But really excited!"

"Good. Try to get some good sleep. I'll get you up in the morning. Good night."

"Night, Mom," I said.

Mom turned out the light and I laid in bed with my eyes open. I stared at the ceiling, which I could see a little bit because the hall light was coming through the crack in the slightly opened door. I thought about each event and visualized each of my routines. Before I knew it, I was asleep.

I awoke to sunlight flooding into my room when my mom opened my window shades. "Wake up, Sweetheart! It's your big day!" I rubbed my eyes. "Time to get in the shower. I'll make your breakfast."

"Okay," I stretched. "I'll be downstairs in a few minutes," I said.

Mom went downstairs, and it was time for me to get to work. I had my whole morning planned out. Shower first, then I'd dry off and put some loose-fitting clothes on, eat some breakfast, have Mom do my hair, then change into my leotard and warm-up. I started on my plan.

While I was walking downstairs to breakfast, Al stopped me on the stairs. "Morning, Rat," she said.

"Hi!" I smiled.

"I have something for you," she said handing me a small box.

"Thanks" I said. "What is it?"

"It's a good-luck gift. Open it."

I opened the small box. Inside was a small silver charm in the shape of a gymnast.

"Cool!" I said. "Thanks, Al! Now all I need is a charm bracelet to put it on."

"Good luck today, Morgan," Al said.

"Thanks, Al."

We walked down to the breakfast table. Mom had oatmeal, fruit, walnuts, coconut water, toast, peanut butter, and all sorts of other healthy foods out for us to choose from. Al and I filled our plates and ate. I heard Jack turn the shower on upstairs. Dad came out of his and Mom's bedroom in his "Gymnastics Dad" t-shirt.

"Good morning, ladies," he said. He kissed Al and I on the tops of our heads.

We said our "good mornings" between bites.

I finished my breakfast and put my dishes in the sink. "Mom, can you do my hair now?"

"Go grab the box of hair stuff then come and sit on the stool," she said

Sitting on the stool in the living room, Mom put gel in my hair and pulled it up tight in a bun. She combed the sides so there weren't any lumps showing, sprayed it with hair spray and put the scrunchie in. Then she sprayed it again. "Okay, all done," she said. "Run upstairs and get your leotard and warm-up on. I'll pack your snack. Oh, and don't stub your toe!"

"Very funny," I said.

I came back down the stairs in all my garb and with my backpack on my shoulder. I carried my water bottle and filled it up with ice and water. On the table was a box a little bit bigger than the one that Allison handed me. "What's this?" I asked.

"Open it," smiled Mom.

I opened the box and inside was a silver charm bracelet! "Oh, thank you!" I cried. "Now I can put the charm that Al gave me on it."

"Good luck today, Honey. We're very proud of you." Mom and Dad came over and gave me a hug. "Okay, now it's time for pictures! Get in the living room."

I posed in my warm-up and leotard for Mom to take pictures. "Are we done yet?" I complained.

"Just one more," Mom said. "Al, get in there. I want the two competitive gymnasts in the family in there." Al walked over and we smiled. "There. Let's go!"

As I walked out of the living room, I glanced at myself in the mirror. I looked like a competitor! My hair was done perfectly, I had my leotard on, and my warm-up over it. I *looked* ready. But I wasn't so sure I *felt* ready!

Chapter 15

GETTING THERE

The coaches wanted us at the meet thirty minutes before we needed to begin warm-up. When we got there, the session before us was still competing. There was a gymnast check-in table.

"What's your name and gym?"

"Morgan from TGC," I answered. I could hear my voice quiver a little. I was nervous!

"316," the lady said. She wrote my number on my hand with a magic marker. I walked back to where my family was waiting for me.

"What number did you get?" asked Al. I showed her my fist. "Ooh, that's a good one," she said. I believed her.

We stayed in the lobby of the high school, just as we were instructed, and waited for our team members to get to the meet. Samantha came in and waved as she got in line at the gymnast check-in. Then I saw Madison, Dakota and Amber. They all got in line. The weird thing was, I didn't see either of our coaches. Little did I know, they were already in the gym preparing for the meet.

A few minutes later, Deb and Stephanie walked into the lobby from the gym and came over to our growing group of teammates and parents. "Good morning, everyone," Deb said. "How are we all doing?" All of us gymnasts started nervous chatter about what interesting thing happened while we were getting ready that morning. I told everyone about my charm bracelet.

"Where's Charlotte?" Deb asked. "Has anyone seen her yet this morning?" No one had seen her. "I'll call her." Deb walked over to a quieter part of the lobby to call Charlotte's mom to see where they were. I guess it was a good thing that we had to get there thirty minutes early!

Deb came back over just as Charlotte and her mom came running in the door. Deb pointed to the gymnast check-in area and they stood in line. When they came over to the team, Charlotte said, "Sorry! I forgot to take off my nail polish off and we had to stop at the store to get some nail polish remover."

"Well, I'm glad that you remembered before you got here," said Deb. "All right, everyone.

It looks like we are all here! Say 'good-bye' to your parents; you won't see them until after the meet."

All the parents hugged their daughters and wished them good luck. They left and went into the stands. Now it was just the coaches and our little team together in the lobby. "Before we go in, does anyone need to use the bathroom?" Stephanie asked.

"I do," said Leslie and Charlotte together.

"Me too," said Madison.

"How about we all go," said Stephanie. We all followed her to the bathroom.

Now we were all ready to enter the gym. We were together as a team, led by our coaches. It felt so official! We stepped into the gym and I gasped and grabbed Gym's arm. "This place is huge!" I said. "There are two vaults, two sets of bars, two beams. Wow!"

"Where's the other floor?" asked Madison.

"There isn't one. I never saw two floors in all of Al's meets," I said. I looked around. The audience was sitting in the bleachers on two sides of the gym. I scanned the bleachers to see where my family was. There they were. *Right. Above. Beam.* What were they doing there? I hoped I wouldn't fall off.

"Girls, let's put our bags on the floor here," Deb said, pointing along the wall by one of the vault runways. "Sit down on the runway. This is where we will warm up." We all sat down and looked around at our new surroundings. "We have something for you."

Deb and Stephanie handed out colorful envelopes. Inside, mine read:

Dear Rat,
  Good luck today! Just keep thinking about the little things

and take your routines one skill at a time, and you'll do great.

"Set your goals high, and don't stop till you get there." -Bo Jackson

-Coach Deb
-Coach Stephanie

"Ok, girls! Time to get warmed up," Deb called to us. I stuffed my card in the front pocket of my backpack and stood up. "Line up on the runway. Give each other some room, and face me."

All of a sudden, a loud voice came over the speaker system. "Ladies, please start your open warm-up."

Deb said, "Go!" Leslie started counting our jumping jacks.

"Be sure you're together," said Coach Stephanie. "Look at your teammates next to you and make sure you're going at the same time."

As we finished the jumping part of our warm up, the loud voice came over the loudspeaker again. "We need one coach from each team to report to the head table for a coaches' meeting." Deb walked over. Stephanie watched over us as we stretched. Deb came back after the meeting and talked to Stephanie. She had a bunch of cards in her hand.

"Girls, once you finish stretching, put your warm-ups back on. Follow Coach Stephanie over to the other side of the gym. That's where you'll start march-in." I went to my bag and put my warm-up on. "Leave your bags where they are, girls. Line up shortest to tallest, just like we practiced in the gym." Samantha was first, then Gym, me, Leslie, Dakota, Amber and Charlotte.

Stephanie led us to a hallway where the other teams were lining up. "Girls, stand like gymnasts," she said. "Follow the team in front of you, and make sure you walk like gymnasts. Just do what they tell you to do and go where they tell you to line up. They will call 'TGC' and that's when you salute, just like we practiced. When they tell you to march to your first event, look for Deb and me and walk over to us. You look great!"

Music started playing across the speakers. "It's time!" Stephanie said. "Walk like gymnasts - and smile!" We followed each other out of the hallway and into the big gym. I pointed my toes as I walked and swung my arms front and back. I was trying not to trip, so I think I forgot to smile… I scanned the crowd for my family and saw them clapping and cheering as we walked past them. My stomach flipped and my hands started to sweat. We stood in a straight line on the floor and waited for the announcer to call our gym. Finally, we heard it.

"TGC!" My whole team saluted at the same time. Arms went up, arms went down. I heard cheering and screaming from the crowd. I smiled. They were cheering for *us*!

The announcer told everyone to stand for the National Anthem. We turned our line to face the huge American flag hanging from the ceiling. I stared at the flag and thought, "I'm standing at my first meet listening to the National Anthem. The crowd is here to watch us." I was confident, excited and nervous all at the same time.

The music stopped. The announcer said, "Gymnasts, please march to your first rotation." I saw Deb and Stephanie motioning for us to march toward them. We stayed in a straight line and walked like gymnasts over to them. They were by beam.

"Here we go, girls. We start on beam!" said Deb.

Chapter 16

WE'RE STARTING ON BEAM?!

"We're starting on beam?!" Amber cried.

"Yes, we're starting on beam," Deb said. "Girls, you can keep your warm-ups on for now. The group on the other beam, flight A, is warming up before you. Once they start competing, we will start to warm up. We are flight B." I watched the other team as they got ready and began their warm up. "Go over to Coach Stephanie. She has your order."

We all sat down obediently in front of Stephanie. She had a bunch of cards in her hand. Each card had one of our names on it, along with spaces for scores on each event. "Charlotte, you're up first," Stephanie said. Charlotte looked scared. "Then Leslie, Morgan, Amber, Madison, Samantha and Dakota."

"Okay, I'm third," I thought. I can handle that. I saw Deb over with Charlotte, trying to make her feel better about going first.

"You're not really first," Deb said. "There is a whole team in front of you. You're just first for our team. Besides, you'll do great. That's why we chose you to go first. You are strong on beam."

Charlotte's face didn't change. She still looked scared.

"Girls, it's time to take your warm-ups off, put them in your bags, and do a few things on the floor to warm up your routines. The other group is about to compete."

We all did as Deb said and started to go over our routines on the floor. I did some handstands and leaps, and went through the dance in my routine.

"Charlotte, time to warm up," Stephanie called. "The rest of you stand in line and get ready." Charlotte went over to the beam and looked at Coach Stephanie with big eyes. "Go ahead, Kiddo," Stephanie said with her finger on the stopwatch. Charlotte climbed up on the beam and warmed up. "Leslie, you're up." Leslie climbed up.

I was next in line. I tried to stand still, but I kept picking up my feet and shaking them. They were getting sweaty, and I didn't want to slide off the beam. Leslie was on her dismount. I stepped forward, ready to mount the beam.

"Okay, Rat," Stephanie said. I climbed up on the beam. It felt weird and smooth; it wasn't the same as our beam at the gym at all. And it felt so high. I put my arms up and kicked to go into my handstand, but it was scary up there! I didn't go all the way up. "Higher, Morgan," I heard Stephanie say. *No kidding.* I did my arabesque and my leap, then fell off the beam. "Get back up there," Stephanie said. I got up and did my jumps and my pivot turns, then my snap turn and my dismount. Phew! I was done!

"Come here, Morgan," Deb called. I walked over to her. "Ok, how did you feel up there?" she asked.

"Shaky and scared," I fessed up.

"That's ok," she said.

"It is?" I asked, perplexed.

"Yes, it is. Now you know how it feels to be up on that beam. It's not new anymore. Now you can go up there and do the routine that you've been doing in the gym."

"But the beam isn't the same," I said.

"Of course it's not the same," she laughed. "It's not the same beam!"

I tried to crack a smile, but I wasn't feeling it. The beam was smooth, high, and weird. There was no way that I could do the routine I always did in the gym on that thing.

"Go visualize your beam routine five times. I want you to stick it in your head," Deb said.

"Okay," I answered.

The rest of the girls continued to warm up. While Dakota was finishing her timed warm-up, the judges came over from the other beam to watch us compete. "Charlotte, get ready," Deb said.

Charlotte stood just off the beam mat waiting for Dakota to finish her warm-up. I stood and stared at her. She looked like a scared little bunny! All of a sudden, the head judge raised a green flag. Charlotte saluted. She stood at the side of the beam, closed her eyes, and took a deep breath. (I held mine.) She swung her leg over and mounted the beam. She got up and did her handstand. It wasn't all the way up, but she stayed on the beam. Then she did the rest of her routine, looking like she was doing it as fast as she could in order to get off the beam as fast as she could. All of a sudden, she did her dismount and was back on the floor. She remembered to salute the judges. We all cheered! "Great job, Char," Deb said. Leslie got ready and stood by the beam. "Morgan, come here," Deb said.

I walked over and stood next to Deb. "Remember, you know what the beam is like now. It's not new. You can do this routine, and do it well. Just do what you've been doing in the gym and think about the skill you're doing as you're doing it. Take your time." By this time, Leslie was finishing up her routine and saluting the judge. "It's time," Deb said. I walked up to the side of the beam.

I picked my feet up one at a time. They were still sweaty. My hands were sweaty. There were butterflies in my stomach. Why do we have to start on beam? Before I knew it, the green flag went up, and so did my arms. I stood next to the beam and mounted. It was as though my body was working without my thinking about it. I kept going, did my dance, and got ready for my handstand. It wasn't until after my handstand that I remembered that I had to think about what I was doing. Forced arch, up, forced arch. Step, step, point. Lift, circle, down, arabesque hold, one gymnastics, two gymnastics… I continued to talk myself through my routine. High kick cartwheel handstand hold… and I landed. I saluted. I stayed on the beam! My team cheered. I heard my mom "whoop" from the crowd. Stephanie and Deb high-fived me and my team congratulated me. I felt pretty good up there - but I felt way better to be on the floor again!

I stood and waited for my score as Amber did her routine. It flashed on a big screen: 8.35. "Hey Rat," said Deb. "Not bad!" I smiled, completely relieved.

Madison got up and did her routine. She fell on her handstand. "Finish strong, Gym!" I cheered. The rest of her routine was good.

As soon as Dakota finished her routine, Deb said, "All right, girls, time to get over to floor!"

Chapter 17

I Thought Floor was Easy!

We had to warm up floor in between the other group's routines. So each time a gymnast finished her routine and saluted, we had to get up in a line across the floor and warm up our skills. Then the judge would yell, "Clear the floor!" and we would have to run off and sit down. Even though we practiced it in the gym at home, it was nerve-wracking and everything went so fast! The cool thing was, the floor was super bouncy! It felt like my rebound out of my round-off back handspring was ten feet high! All of a sudden, it was time to compete. This time, Madison was first.

Madison did a great routine. She even had straight legs on her round-off back handspring at the end of her routine! "Awesome job, Gym!" I gave her a high-five. Charlotte was next. She still looked scared, but not as bad as on beam. Next was Amber, Leslie, and then Samantha, Dakota, then I was last. It was hard to sit and wait for all my teammates to go. All I thought about was wanting to get it over with.

Finally, Dakota was up. Stephanie called me over to talk to her. "Remember, one thing at a time, Rat. Listen to the music and smile out there. You can do it!" Dakota finished her routine and I stood in the corner, waiting for the judge to lift the flag.

And then I forgot which judge to look at! Oh no! Who was going to raise the flag? I settled on one judge, and kept my eye on her. It was Judge Jill from the critique meet! Oh, good. Now I could show her how much I'd improved! Then Judge Jill smiled and pointed at the other judge who was impatiently raising the flag. I turned and saluted. I could feel my face get red and hot as I walked out to the floor and got in my starting position. I noticed that I had to go to the bathroom.

The music started, and so did I. I did my dance, and then my handstand bridge kick over. But I missed the kick over and had to do another one to get back to my feet. I could hear the music, and I was listening to it, but I was not dancing and doing my routine to it! I was behind! I tried to catch up as I went down into my splits to do the down part of my routine, but in doing that I really didn't show my splits. I was rushing through my skills to get on the beat, and it wasn't working! I stood up, did my half turn and my round-off back handspring. Then I did my end pose - after the music ended. I saluted, to the correct judge this time, and walked off the floor hanging my head.

"It's ok, Morgan. You did fine," said Stephanie.

"You finished strong," Gym said.

"No time to wallow, Morgan. We've got to get to vault!"

"But I have to go to the bathroom!" I said.

Chapter 18

HURRY UP AND WAIT

"Does anyone else have to go?" asked Deb.

Three of us raised our hands. "Follow me," said Stephanie. She was walking so fast! "We have to hurry, girls," she said. "They'll be waiting for us on vault when we get back."

I didn't realize just how difficult a competition leotard was to deal with until I had to hurry up and take it off and put it back on during a competition. It really just stuck in place! But I had to hurry! Those long sleeves were the worst!

"Let's go, let's go!" yelled Stephanie. "Be sure to follow me exactly. You don't want to go in front of judges."

When we got back to the vault runway, we found out the the group in front of us was still warming up, so we had to just sit and wait for our turn to warm up. "I thought we had to hurry up," Leslie whispered.

"Sometimes during meets the events get backed up," Deb explained. "But it is our job to make sure we hurry the best we can so we are ready for timed warm-up and competition when the judges are ready for us. Now, listen up for your order. Morgan, Amber, Dakota, Samantha, Madison, Leslie, Charlotte." Ahh! I was first!

At that point, the other group started to compete. The timer came over to talk to Deb and asked how many girls we had on our team so she knew how long to time us. "Girls, time to do a couple of sprints, and then a row of nice, tight handstands. Be sure not to touch the board so the time doesn't start before we're ready."

We lined up and followed each other sprinting down the runway. Then we did our handstands. "Be tight, girls!" Stephanie said. She stopped each of us in a handstand and tried to pull our feet apart to make sure that we were squeezing. When we were finished she said, "Line up in your competition order. And be sure to use the yellow tape measure, not the white one. The yellow one is measured to the mat and the other one is measured to the vault on the other end of the runway."

I found my spot on the runway. Deb yelled, "Do a stretch jump! Go!" from down at the mat. Even though we could all do our vaults by ourselves, Deb stood there during warm-ups just to be safe.

I ran hard down the runway, hit the board, and did a stretch jump up to the mat. The board was hard! Deb motioned to Amber to go next. "Rat, make sure you keep you chest up on the board. Do a handstand flat back next time." I nodded and ran back to the end of the line. My teammates did their vaults. Charlotte finished her stretch jump and Deb motioned for me to go. I ran, tried to hit the board hard and tried to keep my chest up. I did a handstand flat back. "Good," Deb said. Stay tight when you land. One more."

I did one more vault, and then stood down at the end of the runway with Stephanie. "Okay, Rat, find your spot on the tape measure," she said. "Stand to the side of the runway and wait for the judge. You ready?"

"I guess so. The board feels weird."

"Well, it's a new board, so it's probably a little bit stiff. Just run hard and hit it hard. You'll be okay." she said.

I nodded and stared at the judges at the end of the runway. The green flag went up, I saluted. I stepped to the middle of the runway and dragged my big toe from the tape measure to to make sure I had the exact right spot. I took a deep breath, and started running. I hit the board hard, but forgot to keep my chest up. I reached for the mat and rolled over to my back instead of hitting a handstand. I landed on the mat, slid off, and saluted to the judges. Deb walked with me on the way back. "You have one more vault, Morgan. You can do it. Keep your chest up on the board and show them what you can do!"

"Come on, Rat!" I heard my teammates cheer for me.

The green flag went up. I saluted, dragged my big toe to my starting place, and ran. I hit the board, this time not as hard, but I did keep my chest up. I hit a handstand, and landed flat on my back. I sat up, slid off the mat, and saluted.

"Much better!" Deb said. She patted me on the back as she got the board ready for Amber.

"Nice job, Rat. You definitely improved on the second vault," Stephanie said.

"Thanks," I said. "Come on, Amber!" I yelled as she saluted.

Chapter 19

LAST EVENT

We finished up on vault and then rotated to bars. "Girls, here's your order," Deb said. "Samantha, Charlotte, Leslie, Morgan, Madison, Dakota, Amber. Stand in your order and be ready to start. Don't touch the bar!"

"Girls, as soon as time starts, Samantha needs to get on the bar. Pay attention to the person in front of you so that you get on the bar as soon as she gets off. Do a full routine, and then if we have time you can work on problem areas," explained Stephanie.

"Time to go," Deb said. Samantha did her glide swing and continued her routine. She over rotated her front mill circle, so Deb helped her back up on the bar. She finished her routine. Charlotte did her routine, and made it through. Leslie was up, then I was next. I watched her so I could do my glide swing as soon as she finished her dismount. She landed, so I started my glide. But just as I jumped for the bar, Leslie fell on her butt on her dismount. I had to stop my glide swing so I wouldn't kick her in the head. She got up off the floor, and I had to start over. I had to hurry! I did my pullover, then fell forward for my front hip circle and piked too soon, so I fell. I had to do another pullover to get back up on the bar. I went through the rest of my routine, but it wasn't that great.

I must have looked worried when I got off the bar. "It's okay, Morgan. Slow down and take it one skill at a time," Stephanie said. "If we have time, do another front hip circle."

"Okay," I said.

"One minute left," the timer said.

One minute? That's it? Amber hadn't even gone yet! I wasn't going to have a chance to do my front hip circle again!

We all got back in line to see if we could get in one more turn before time was up. I stood behind Leslie and watched her, bending and straightening my knees one at a time, hoping my teammates would hurry up so I could go. As Charlotte got on the bar, we heard, "Time!" *Time was up. I didn't get to make my front hip circle! Oh no!*

Deb must have seen the freaked-out look on my face. "It's okay, Morgan. Sometimes you're not going to have a good warm-up, and you have to compete anyway. It's one of the things that makes gymnasts tough," she said. "You can do it. A bad warm-up doesn't equal a bad routine."

Samantha was up. Her routine was pretty good, although she did stop between her back hip circle and her under swing dismount. But she stayed on the bar. Charlotte and Leslie both went in front of me, and while they were doing their routines, all I could think about was my front hip circle. Was I going to make it? Next thing I knew, Stephanie was tapping me on the shoulder. "Rat, you're up! Take it one thing at a time, and you'll be fine."

I stood by the bar and waited for the judge. She saluted. I saluted. I stepped up to the bar and did my glide swing. *Straight arms, feet up, extend, round.* I came back to the floor to do my pullover. *Straight legs, point toes, chest up.* Next was my front hip circle. *Chest up, lift heels, wait, and pike.* I made a great front hip circle, and I was able to cast right out of it! *Hips up, leg through and hold.* I was ready for my mill circle. *Chest up, big step forward, switch hands, lift.* Wow, my routine was going great! I did my cut back, cast, back hip circle, under swing dismount. I even stuck my landing! Wow!

I heard cheers coming from my team and coaches. I saluted and smiled. "Yeah, Rat! Great job!" My teammates gave me high-fives. So did Deb and Stephanie. What a relief!

Bars was over, and even though I had a bad warm-up, my routine was great! I looked up at my score, and I got an 8.75! Not only was bars over, by my first meet was over too. I was done! I sat with my team and cheered for the rest of my teammates while they finished their routines.

Chapter 20

Awards

When we all finished competing, Deb said, "Girls, come over here and sit down. We're going to watch the rest of the competitors compete and wait until they're finished before we go over to awards."

"Why?" asked Amber.

"Because it's good sportsmanship," said Deb. "If we were the last team competing, would you want everyone else to leave and make us compete all by ourselves in here?"

"No," we all said.

"You all did a great job today. It was a solid first meet. We have some things to get better at, but overall, we're pleased with how you girls did. Good job!" Deb smiled.

Once all the other gymnasts were finished competing, we followed the coaches to the awards room. There was a podium with the numbers 1, 2, and 3 on it, and behind it was a bunch of balloons. All the teams sat down together in front of the podium and the parents sat in bleachers behind us.

It took awhile for them to hand all the awards out, but it was fun! Each of us from our gym got an award for an event. I got fourth place for my bar routine! And we all got medals for all-around.

Then they handed out team awards. There were about ten teams at the meet, and we came in 5th. We didn't get a trophy, but they called us to come up and salute for the crowd. All of our parents cheered for us and took our pictures when we saluted. We all decided that next time we'd get a trophy!

"Great job, Morgan," my mom hugged me after awards.

"Thanks, Mom," I said.

Dad came over and gave me a big hug. I even got a high-five from Jack.

Al said, "Well done on bars, Rat. You really pulled it together."

"Thanks," I smiled. "Can we go to dinner with Madison and her family?" I asked.

"We already have plans to do just that," Mom said.

"All right!" I said. "Where are they?"

"They're over by the bleachers," Mom said. "We'll see them as we walk out the door."

At dinner, Gym and I talked nonstop about what happened at the meet. How nervous we were, and how fun it was (kind of!) to compete, and how we were going to do better next time. Al explained to us how Deb and Stephanie were going to go over our routines and give us a piece of paper that had corrections on it so that we could focus on those during practice for the next meet.

"I can't wait to get back to practice! I want to fix my mistakes and get better scores. I want to get a 9.0 this year!" I told Gym.

"Me too! Let's help each other get there!" We gave each other a high-five and did our secret handshake.

Now I get what Al meant by wanting to beat herself each time she competed. She wanted to get better and better so she could keep getting higher and higher scores!

Meet number one down, many, many more to go!

Coach's Corner

Preparing for your first meet can be exciting, but it can also make you nervous. Your coaches will prepare you well in the gym and make some practices feel as much like a meet as possible at times so you can feel what it is like to be on the competition floor. Of course, practice can never be exactly like a meet, so it will be a little bit different.

In our gym, we have a critique meet for all the teams so they can showcase their routines before a judge and their families before going out to a real meet for the first time that season. This helps all gymnasts, of all levels, to feel what it's like to compete before the big day. This critique meet helps young compulsory gymnasts as well as upper-level optional gymnasts. Every season is a new experience, no matter how experienced a gymnast is.

You may have noticed that Allison used a lot of visualization before it was her turn to compete. This really helps gymnasts focus on her routine and the skills that she has to do. Being able to visualize yourself in the actual competition location is especially helpful. If you can get to your meets a little bit early and look out on the floor and see what apparatus you'll be on, and then visualize your routines there, you will be ahead of the game.

Remember that competition doesn't come naturally to all gymnasts; it's a process. You will improve each season throughout your competitive career, and the goal is that you will be the best you have ever been at competing at the end of your career. It's important to remember that you won't know it all at the beginning; you will learn from your experience along the way.

Happy competing!

DRILLS TO SKILLS

One of the hardest things to do on beam in level 3 is a good handstand. It can be scary to go all the way up to handstand on a high beam. But handstands are very important skills that all competitive gymnasts must master in order to move on in gymnastics. Here are some things you can do to help you make doing a handstand easier and more comfortable.

Handstands on low beam. Practice going all the way up to handstand and holding it with a spotter. This can help you feel where vertical is so when you're on high beam, you know when you're there.

Handstands on low beam against a wall or stable mat. This drill can help you feel how hard you have to kick in order to make the handstand up to vertical.

Handstands on low beam, kicking over so you practice turning and falling safely. If you kick up to handstand and learn how to fall before you try it on the high beam, then you will be more comfortable when it's time to do it by yourself.

Handstands at the end of the high beam.

Here, you will be able to get used to the height of the beam, but if you go over, you can practice turning and landing on a nice, soft mat.

Keep in mind that courage and bravery doesn't always come naturally in every gymnast. However, if you ask your coach for some drills to help make you more comfortable, you will soon become more brave and you'll be kicking up to a vertical handstand in no time!

Glossary

Back Half: a back flip with a half twist

Back Handspring: a tumbling skill where you jump off two feet, arch backward to push off your hands and finish back on your feet

Back Handspring: a tumbling skill where you jump off two feet, arch backward to push off your hands, and land on both feet together

Back Handspring Stepout: a tumbling skill where you jump off two feet, arch backward to push off your hands, split your legs, and land on one foot, then the other

Blind Change: s skill on bars where you swing and turn to face the other direction on top of the bar

Blind Landing: a landing, facing forward, where the gymnast cannot see the floor before she lands

Cast Handstand: a skill on bars where you begin in a front support and end up in a hollow body position all the way to handstand

Compete: the act of performing your routines in front of a judge for a score

Compulsory: levels 3-5 in gymnastics where everyone competing performs the same routines

Complex: a series of basic skills used together to create a warm-up or workout for an event

Deductions: the points taken off a routine in a competition

Double Back Flyaway: a skill where you perform two backwards saltos in one flip off the bar for a dismount

Double Full: a skill where you perform two twists in one flip

Drill: skill or part of a skill that helps to improve technique or a larger skill

Free Hip Handstand: a back hip circle without touching your hips to the bar, opening your shoulders so you go to handstand

Front Hip Circle: a bar skill where you begin in a front support, circle forward around the bar and end up in front support

Front Mill Circle: a bar skill where you split the bar and circle forward around the bar

Full Split: in leaps and jumps, when the split is 180 degrees

Full Turn: a turn on one foot that goes 360 degrees

Full Twist: a flip with a 360 degree twist in the middle

Giant: a circle on the bar where you begin in a handstand and swing in a straight line all the way around the bar back to handstand, keeping your arms straight overhead the entire time

Glide Kip: a bar skill where you swing under the bar, bring your toes to the bar, then pull yourself up to a front support

Glide Swing: a bar skill where you swing under the bar (the first part of a glide kip)

Grips: leather worn on a gymnast's hands to help her stay on the bars

Half Pirouette: from a handstand, turn both hands to turn the body so you are facing the other direction

Handstand: a position where you stand vertically on your hands

Handstand Flat Back: a vault where after you jump on the board, you do a handstand and fall to your back in a tight body position (the level 3 competitive vault)

Handstand Forward Roll: a tumbling skill where you perform a handstand then roll forward out of it

Head Judge: the judge in a panel on each event that raises the flag and the gymnast salutes to

Injury Prevention: exercises to help strengthen small muscles, tendons and ligaments so injury does not happen as easily

Layout Flyaway: a bar dismount where you perform a tap swing and let go of the bar to do a straight-body salto to your feet

Layout Step Out: a skill where you perform a back handspring step out with no hands

Leap Pass: a combination of dance skills

Leg Lift: a conditioning move where you hang straight down from the bar and lift your toes to the bar

Level 8: the eighth of ten levels in USA Gymnastics

Long Hang Kip: a kip on the high bar

Meet Run-Through: a (usually) shortened practice where you and your team run through your routines, usually before a competition

Meet Warm-up: a set warm-up that a team does to warm-up for a meet

Mock Meet: also known as a "critique meet" where you and your team perform your routines in front a a judge before the season officially starts for experience

Mount: the skill that gets you onto an apparatus

One-and-a-Half-Turn: a turn on toe that is 540 degrees

Open Warm-up: the first part of a meet where gymnasts warm-up on the floor to prepare for the meet

Optionals: the term used for levels 6-elite; those competitors that make up their own routines

Pike Tsuk: a Tsukahara vault (half-on, flip off) ina pike position

Pit Mat: a thick mat, usually 36 inches, where you compete a handstand flat back

Pivot Turn: a turn done on two feet when they are in relevé lock

Press Handstand: a skill where you press your shoulders over your hands and either straddle or pike up into a handstand position

Pullover: a skill on bars where you begin in a hanging position (or on the floor under the low bar) and lift your hips to the bar and circle backwards around the bar until you finish in a front support

Punch Front: a front tuck from a run or out of another flip

Regionals: a post-season meet where the best gymansts in your state's region compete

Release Move: a skill on bars where you let go of the bar and then catch it again

Rotation: the group a gymnast competes on each event with

Round-off: a skill where you begin like a cartwheel, but you bring your feet together in the middle and land on two feet

Runway: the place on vault where one runs to the vault

Season: the part of the year during which you compete

Series: a connection of two skills in a row; most often associated with an acro connection on beam

Set: to put the equipment on a specific height or distance for a gymnast

Setting: the height or distance equipment is placed for a gymnast

Single-leg Shoot Through: a bar skill where you cast and place one foot through your hands

Sprint: a short fast run, as on vault

Squat-on: a bar skill where you tuck your knees so both feet land on the low bar between your hands, usually to catch the high bar

Stall Bar: a bar that looks like a ladder next to a wall where gymnasts can do conditioning skills

Standing Back Tuck: a single salto in the tuck position from a stand

State: a post-season meet where the best gymnasts in the state compete

Switch Leap: a leap where you kick one leg up, then switch your legs in the air and end in full split

Timed Warm-up: at a meet, the set amount of time a gymnast gets to warm up her routine

Tuck Tsuk: a Tsukahara vault (half-onn, flip off) in the tuck position

Upgrade: to work a more difficult version of a skill

Vault Table: the vaulting apparatus

Vegan: a diet where you do not eat any animal products

Vegetarian: a diet where you do not eat any meat

Yurchenko: a vault skill where you perform a round-off onto the springboard, a back handspring onto the vault table and a salto before landing on the floor (see *Gym Rats: Toe Jam* for more detailed information)

About the Author

The youngest of eleven children, Mary Reiss Farias grew up on a farm in Corcoran, Minnesota. At the age of five, she began gymnastics. Loving the sport, she continued at North Shore Gymnastics Association in Long Lake, Minnesota until she graduated from high school. Good grades and her level 10 skill set earned her a scholarship to the University of Arizona in Tucson where she competed all four years of her eligibility. Mary then spent the next decade coaching, among other occupations. In 2012, she and her husband, Marc, opened their own gymnastics training center in Tucson,

Arizona, called Tucson Gymnastics Center. Marc and Mary have one daughter. This is Mary's fourth book.

Other books by Mary Reiss Farias:

Gym Rats: Basic Training
Book 1 in the *Gym Rats* series

Gym Rats: Toe Jam
Book 2 in the *Gym Rats* series

Gym Rats: Moving Up
Book 3 in the *Gym Rats* series

Other projects by IrisBlu Publishing:

Home Fire: Sarah and Charlie by Nancy Ann
Book 1 in the *Home Fire* series

Home Fire: The Journey Home by Nancy Ann
Book 2 in the *Home Fire* series

Home Fire: The Big Year By Nancy Ann
Book 3 in the *Home Fire* Series

For teens and young adults, the *Home Fire* series follows Sarah as she moves to the woods of northern Minnesota. Be a part of her interesting journey as she meets many friends and obstacles along the way.

With All Due Respect

Do you know an older American with a great story? IrisBlu Publishing is collecting the stories of our older Americans to be published in magazine form. These stories should be written by Americans 70 years of age or older and should capture what life was like in the early decades of the 20th Century. For more imformation, please visit www.withallduerespectproject.com.

IrisBlu

publishing

Tucson, AZ